FOR LUNCH

JACOB SINGHAVONG

ILLUSTRATED BY: RATU MEGAWANGI

To my family and Lao community

"The beauty of the world lies in the diversity of its people."
-Unknown

Sabaidee, my name is Kop. I'm seven years old.
Today, I start first grade.
Before I leave for school, Mae prepares my lunch.

Paw drops me off and I run to the playground to play with my friends.

At school, I see my friends getting dropped off.
And look! There's Sarah. She's my best friend.

In Ms. Jocelyn's class, we learn about different cultures around the world to prepare for Culture Day.

A family from Asia eats chicken feet and rice.

Another family enjoys a bowl of fish head soup around a bamboo table.

Look! A plate of snails! This is a French dish called escargot.

Learning about food makes me hungry!
I can't help but wonder what Mae packed
me for lunch today.

Ring!

Ring!

RING!

It's finally lunch time!

Time to eat! My friend Sarah has a ham and cheese sandwich with potato chips. My other friend, Vanh, got a yummy pizza from the cafeteria.

In my lunch pail I see a container of
khao niao—sticky rice and seen hang—
Lao beef jerky. Woah! This is an epic lunch!

My friends make weird faces. Tin asks,
"Why don't you eat normal food?"

This made me very sad and embarrassed to bring Lao food to school again.

"No sticky rice today?" Sarah wondered.
"I loved the smell of your sticky rice because it reminds
me of my grandma's cooking."

"My family enjoys cooking and eating Chinese food," continued Sarah.

"My grandma makes the best steamed pork buns. I wish I was brave enough to bring them."

I enjoy learning about how similar Sarah's culture is to mine and how delicious the food sounds! It made me realize how much I miss Lao food for lunch. "I have an idea!"

"I'll bring you some khao niao!" I said excitedly. "And you bring your grandma's pork buns so we can trade lunches."

The next day, Sarah and I swap lunches
and try each other's food.

Her eyes grow huge when she tries
khao niao muk muong.
I think she enjoys it!

Our friends come over, even Tin, and are interested in what we're eating.

They ask if we can bring them some to try tomorrow. Both Sarah and I smiled at each other and said,"Sure!"

Sarah and I ask Ms. Jocelyn if we can bring some of our cultural food to share with the class. She says, "Yes, of course!"

"Students, tomorrow is Culture Day, please bring food from your culture to share."

The following day, we enjoyed different cultural foods from our classmates. I brought khao niao and seen hang. My friend Sarah brings her grandma's famous Chinese pork buns.

Another friend brings Swedish meatballs and potatoes. We even got to try fried grasshoppers!

This was such a fun day at school!
I can't wait to share more of my
favorite Lao food for lunch.

Lao Words
used in the book

ສະບາຍດິ
Sabaidee

(sah-bye-di)
Hello, how are you?

ແມ່
Mae

(mae)
Mom/Mother

ພໍ່
Paw

(paw)
Dad/Father

ເຂົ້າໜຽວ
Khao Niao

(kao-ne-yo)
Sticky rice

ຊີ້ນແຫ້ງ
Seen Hang

(seen-hang)
Lao beef jerky

ເຂົ້າໜຽວໝາກມ່ວງ
Khao Niao Mak Muong

(khao-ne-yo-muk-moo-ong)
Sticky rice & mango

ABOUT THE AUTHOR

Jacob Phonesavanh Singhavong is a first-generation Laotian American who is passionate about the field of education, social justice, and his Lao culture. His passion for cultural preservation, diversity, and equity within education became the inspiration for his first children's book. He possesses a B.A. in Early Childhood Studies and is currently working towards his Master of Social Work.

Jacob has served in various roles within education as an early childhood educator, school social work intern, and day camp director. Serving in these roles have highlighted the significance of anti-bias curriculum, culturally responsive practices, and equitable resources within the field of education. In his spare time, Jacob enjoys traveling, playing the piano, singing, and cooking his favorite Laotian dishes.

A WORD BY THE AUTHOR:

Sabaidee! Thank you for joining me in telling the story of Kop and his favorite Lao foods. This book is a love letter to the Lao community and individuals who have shared similar experiences. Your voice truly matters. So if you enjoyed this story, I would greatly appreciate if you would leave a review on Amazon or any site my book is available on. Your kind feedback is very appreciated and important to me.

In gratitude,
Jacob Singhavong

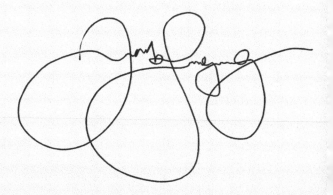

Printed in the USA
CPSIA information can be obtained
at www.ICGtesting.com
LVHW060355151223
766589LV00012B/146